The Complete Works of

O'Carolan

IRISH HARPER & COMPOSER (1670~1738)

Ossian Publications

Music origination by Routledge & Kegan Paul, by permission.

The publishers wish to thank the following institutions and individuals for permission to reprint items from their collections and for their general assistance:

The National Library of Ireland for pages from John Lee's 'A Favourite Collection...'. Queen's University, Belfast, for pages from the Bunting MSS, Mulholland's 'Collection of Ancient Irish Airs' and Neal's 'Collection of the Most Celebrated Irish Tunes . . . . .'.
Capt. A.A.C. Farquharson of Invercauld & Torloisk for tune No. 214 (Captain O'Neill) from the MacLean Clephane MS ©.
The Record Library of Raidió Telefís Éireann.
Professor Aloys Fleischmann .
Cork City & County Libraries.
Gael Linn for permission to reproduce Gráinne Yeats' introduction.
Special thanks to Nicholas Carolan of the Irish Traditional Music Archive, Dublin.
Design and lay-out by John Loesberg.
Cover: 'Carolan the Harper' by Francis Bindon (National Gallery of Ireland).
Cover Design by Joe Gervin.
Ossian Publications, P.O. Box 84, Cork, Ireland.
Printed by Lee Press, Cork.

ISBN 0 946005 16 8

Contents

Carolan — from the painting by J.C. Timbrell, 1844.

Turlough Carolan (1670-1738)

Turlough Carolan, itinerant harper and, perhaps, Ireland's only true national composer, lived through a dismal period in Irish history. His life span coincided with the time when the Penal Laws were at their height and he was born less than thirty years after the final destruction by Cromwell of the old Gaelic order.

In 1691 when Carolan was 21 years old, the defeat at the Battle of Aughrim put an end to any Irish hopes of maintaining independence or religious freedom. The Penal Code began in 1695, and continued with full force right through Carolan's life, and for many years after his death in 1738. These laws were designed to force the Catholic Irish either to abandon their religion or else to be deprived of their property and of all chance of education. It is quite extraordinary that, against this background of the ever-increasing oppression of his own people, Turlough Carolan was able to lead a successful life, and to produce much new and individual music, and that he should have been universally popular amongst all the people of Ireland, whether of Gaelic or non-Gaelic stock.

He started with few advantages. His father was a small subsistence farmer in Co. Meath, where Carolan was born, but when he was fourteen years old the family moved to Co. Roscommon, and Carolan senior took up employment with Mrs McDermott Roe of Ballyfarnon. She was a good friend to Carolan throughout his lifetime, and it was to her house that he eventually returned when he was dying, wishing to end his life near to his dearest friend and oldest patron.

When Carolan was eighteen years old he caught smallpox, and though he recovered from the disease, it left him completely blind. The matter of finding a gainful occupation was then difficult, but he turned to music, and the harp. Mrs McDermott Roe had him taught the instrument, and when he was deemed ready to begin his profession, she provided him with a harp, a horse and a helper to guide him.

Many of the Irish harpers were blind, for music was one of the few professions in which sight was not essential. Though it might be thought that a blind man would have great difficulty in finding his way around a harp, the instrument is in fact largely played by feel. And in the case of the wire-strung Irish harp, the strings were set very close together, so that the accurate placing of nails can have presented few difficulties. A blind harper was always accompanied by a helper, who acted as guide and carried the harp; and since the harping tradition was a wholly oral one, it was, of course, not necessary to be able to read music.

When he began his career, after three years study, Carolan had no thought in his mind about composing. He was a player only, and not even a very good one, for eighteen years of age was much too late to begin on any harp, and particularly on the wire-strung Irish harp. Carolan's playing, therefore, was always scorned by his fellow-harpers and never highly regarded, either, by the patrons for whom he played. The Irish harp, even in its decline, was still in the 17th century the supreme instrument in Ireland, and the harpers were the inheritors of an old and aristocratic tradition that had once been the admiration of Europe. Families would have a harp or two in the house, much as we keep a piano nowadays, and the members of the family all played a little, or even more than a little. The visit of a professional player therefore was welcomed eagerly, and a high standard was expected.

The first house that Carolan visited on his travels was that of George Reynolds of Lough Sgur, in Co. Leitrim. Whatever he played cannot have been very good, for Reynolds advised him to try his skill at composing, saying that he 'might make a better hand of his tongue than his fingers'. Then, according to the story, Carolan composed his first song 'Sí Beag is Sí Mór', based on a local legend about a war between two fairy armies. Squire Reynolds liked it very much and thus encouraged the young harper to turn his talents more in the direction of song writing.

From this beginning, Carolan continued to compose throughout his life. Had he not begun to write music, it is certain that his name would be unknown today, for the band of itinerant harpers was a numerous one and an indifferent performer would stand no chance of achieving name or fame. Most of his music was written for his patrons, or their relatives, and his method was to compose a piece while travelling, so that it was ready for performance by the time he reached his destination.

In writing his songs, Carolan composed the music first, and then thought up words to go with the tune. This is, of course, a reversal of the usual procedure in song writing, in which the words come first. More important, it marked a fundamental reversal of a centuries' old tradition. Music was always very important in Irish society and harp music in particular, but it had always taken second place to poetry. The words were more important than the music, a phenomenon that is still evident to the present day in the field of Irish folk song. "Abair amhrán", not "Can amhrán" is still the injunction of a folksinger, the words are all-important, the tune, however beautiful, is subordinate.

Carolan was a poor poet, because he was primarily a musician and it is through his music, therefore, that he survives, not through his poems. That so much of his music has survived to the present day is a reflection both of its distinctive nature and also of the unusual position Carolan occupied in the Ireland of his day.

In any country there tends to be a division in the musical scene. On the one hand there is the art music composed by the musician trained to that end, and performed by trained professional musicians. On the other hand, there is folk music that is not composed by anyone in particular, but grows out from the natural occupations and inclinations of the ordinary people. In the Ireland of Carolan's time, however, this normal division was complicated by the existence, set in between art music and folk music, of a third musical tradition. This was the music of the harpers, the last remnant of what had once been the art music of the Gaelic nation. The harpers, who had themselves been the art musicians of Gaelic culture, acted as a bridge between the two other kinds of music. It seems probable that the music of the harpers before Carolan's time did not disappear. It merely was absorbed by the oral folk tradition, and is still played and sung today. Who else could have written such melodies as 'An Raibh tú ag an gCarraig', or 'An Chúilfhionn'? Only the harpers had the necessary musical discipline and training to compose such complex and intricate melodies. This anonymous music fits happily for the most part into the repertoire of traditional music. Carolan's music, however, does not fit, because its whole flavour is different. He was not content to be a bridge, but crossed to the other side. He imitated contemporary art style composition so successfully that his music is instantly recognizable amongst the jigs and airs of traditional music. We know a Carolan tune when we hear one.

The three influences at work on Carolan, are to be seen on examination of his music. Folk melody is the weakest of these, but there are a few melodies such as 'Elizabeth McDermott Roe' which are pure folk in style. His inherited harping tradition is to be seen in many tunes, for example, 'Miss Crofton', or 'Sir Arthur Shaen'. Sometimes these two influences come together and we get such beautiful melodies as 'Scarúint na gCompánach' and 'Traolach Óg'. But the strongest influence was that of the music of contemporary Italian composers. According to his friend and patron Charles O'Conor "Vivaldi charmed him and with Corelli he was enraptured". He greatly admired Geminiani, whom he almost certainly met towards the end of his life, when that composer was living in Dublin. Many of his tunes attempt Italian forms, with sequences and imitations. Some of his longer pieces have a quick jig added as a coda, in the manner of Corelli, as for example, 'James Betagh'.

On occasion in his efforts to copy the Italian style, Carolan got lost in extravaganzas of phrases, so that it is sometimes difficult to find a tune amongst all the imitations and sequences. He obviously had a very good ear, and a facility in writing melody, but he lacked the musical training that would have enabled him to use his gifts to the best advantage.

It is a great pity that Carolan's music has survived largely in the form of one-line melody, so that we know little about how he accompanied or harmonised his airs. The rare book of his music, however, of which the National Library in Dublin possesses the only copy known to exist, suggests very strongly, that in this respect he followed closely the traditional harping techniques in which he himself had been trained. The music as set out in the National Library book could be the general way in which Carolan played it: it affords us therefore a valuable insight into the style of harp playing that he inherited from the old tradition.

It cannot be stated definitely what this book is, because several pages including the title page are missing. Until recently it was thought that it was published c.1721 by the brothers John and William Neal of Christchurch Yard in Dublin. Recent research has shown however, that the paper is not older than 1743. It seems from available evidence that it is almost certainly a copy of a book known to have been published in 1748 by Carolan's harper son in collaboration with Dr Delany of Dublin University. No copy of this publication has ever been found. If this incomplete book is indeed a copy of the 1748 publication, then the arrangement of the music provides a valuable clue, not alone as to how Carolan played, but also to traditional harping style as a whole. The music ('John Betagh' and 'Sir Arthur Shaen',) has a strange sound to ears trained in modern arrangement. The melodies are accompanied by a single-line bass, and there is an absence of conventional harmony. On only one or two occasions in the entire book are more than two notes sounded together. But the most unusual feature is the way the bass moves all the time, sometimes in octaves with the treble and often either anticipating or echoing the melody line.

There is little detailed information about Carolan's life. He married a certain Mary Maguire of Co. Fermanagh. They had six daughters as well as the son mentioned earlier. They lived on a small farm near Mohill, Co. Leitrim, and Carolan was perforce often absent.

Mary Maguire died in 1733, and Carolan wrote a fine elegy lamenting her death, though there is no music for the poem. Most of his seven children are shadowy figures, though some facts regarding Carolan's life were ascertained from one of his granddaughters. His son, though a harper, had no talent for either playing or composition and ended his days teaching the harp in London, where he fled, taking with him one of his father's harps and another man's wife.

Turlough Carolan spent most of his time travelling around Ireland, and this must have been a hard life. Imagine this blind musician, travelling on horseback, over the mud roads, accompanied by his helper, also on horseback, to guide him and to carry his harp. Some of the better off players travelled in style, some had not even a companion.

Travelling in bad weather must have been slow and miserable. Indeed, Arthur O'Neill describes such an occasion — "At length I stole away to . . . Crogan, Co. Roscommon, about seven miles or under, and got the most uncommon wetting I ever experienced, and Hannon (my guide) was crying with the wet and cold he suffered in that short journey . . . I was shortly afterwards afflicted with such severe rheumatism that I lost power over two of my left hand fingers . . . ".

It is not to be wondered at that with such a hard life many of the harpers drank too much. There are many stories about harpers' liking for whiskey and Carolan was no exception to the general rule. His temperament was cheerful and gregarious, and he had plenty of friends with whom he drank and celebrated. Charles McCabe, for whom 'Scarúint na gCompánach' was written, was a frequent companion. He also met an occasional enemy, as can be seen by his encounter with David Murphy, harper to Lord Mayo, composer of 'Tiarna Mhaigh Eo'. Murphy had a great opinion of himself, because he once played before King Louis XIV of France. This made him conceited, and his behaviour to his colleagues was such that they heartily disliked him. One day, Murphy came into the inn where Carolan was, and said that Carolan's tunes were like bones without beef. "Damn me" says Carolan, "But I'll compose a tune before I quit you, and you may put what beef you please on the bones of it". With that he seized Murphy by the hair of the head, dragged and kicked him through the room unmercifully, during which time Murphy's screeches could be heard at a great distance: Carolan saying to him while he was roaring "put beef to that air, you puppy". And it's likely, according to the account, that if it were not through some interference he would not leave a drop (of blood) in Murphy . *(Memoirs of Arthur O'Neill).*

As well as harpers and poets, Carolan had friends in high places. Jonathan Swift held him in high esteem, and often had him to play at St. Patrick's Deanery; presumably it is from this period that we may trace the tune called 'Squire Woods' Lamentation on the Refusal of his Halfpence'. The Dean was so taken with another lively song called 'O'Rourke's Feast' that with Carolan's help he translated it into English. In its original form, a Gaelic poem by the Leitrim poet Hugh McGauran, it was often performed by Carolan during those evenings with Jonathan Swift. Relations between the two men seem to have been on a fairly free and easy basis; we are told that once, when reproved by the Dean for being drunk on the road, Carolan replied in verse to the general effect that, whatever the clergy might say to others about drink, it was clear that they themselves never died of thirst.

There are many tales and anecdotes told about Carolan, some more credible than others. The picture that emerges is of a man whom we might call 'a bit of a character'. He was cheerful and outgoing, and possessed of a quick temper. He enjoyed ridiculous stories and practical jokes, and he loved to play backgammon, a game at which he had great skill. He was proud of himself as a man and as a musician and regarded himself as the equal of the patrons for whom he played and composed. He was an Irish-speaking Catholic who never forsook his own people, but at the same time performed impartially for the families of both Gael and Gall.

There is little more to tell, except to speak of his death and funeral. When he felt that his end was approaching, he made his way back to Ballyfarnon, to his old friend Mrs. McDermott Roe. When she came to welcome him at the door of the house, he spoke to her, and said "Tháinic mé anseo, taréis a ndeachas tríd, chun bás d'fháil ins an mbaile fá dheireadh, mar a bhfuaras an chéad fhoghlaim agus an chéad ghearrán". *

Mrs. McDermott brought him inside and gave him a drink of whiskey. When he felt a little stronger, he took up his harp for the last time, and played for her his 'Farewell to Music'. He was ill for about a week, and was nursed devotedly by the members of the household. After his death, he was waked for four days, and crowds of people came from all over Ireland to pay their respects. It was probably a fairly cheerful occasion, for there was plenty of whiskey, and many musicians attended. It would have pleased Carolan that his wake was a lively one, reflecting his own life and character. On the fifth day after his death, Carolan's funeral took place, and he was buried in the McDermott Roe family vault in Kilronan churchyard.

Though Carolan's music is light and unimportant when viewed from the point of view of a large-scale composition, yet it is an amazing achievement. For it came from a man who was blind, could neither read nor write music, and who had no formal training in composition. One can only speculate as to what he might have written had he enjoyed a formal education such as that of Henry Purcell, his own contemporary. As it is, he bridged the gap between continental art music on the one hand, and the Gaelic harp and folk music on the other. In tunes such as 'Mabel Kelly' or the 'Farewell', he took his own harp style, added the wistful haunting quality of folk melody and combined these with his newly gained knowledge of art music. At his best he wrote music that is distinctively Irish, yet has an international flavour as well. It is this achievement that suggests that Turlough Carolan does indeed deserve the title of Ireland's national composer.

Gráinne Yeats

---

* I came here after all I've gone through, to die at home at last, in the place where I got my first teaching and my first horse.

Early Printed Sources

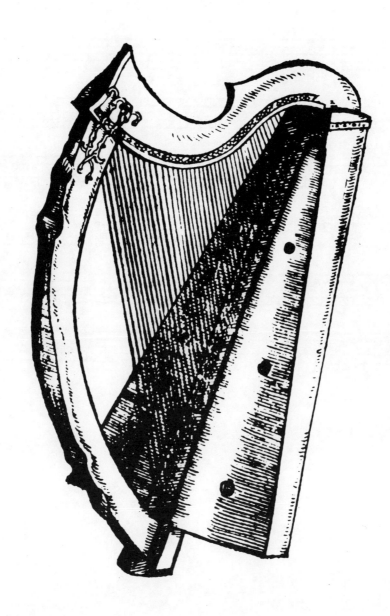

8

(25)

John & William Neal: *A Collection of the Most Celebrated Irish Tunes proper for the Violin, German Flute or Hautboy*, Dublin 1724 (Queen's Univ., Belfast).

John & William Neal: *A Collection of the Most Celebrated Irish Tunes proper for the Violin, German Flute or Hautboy*, Dublin 1724 (Queen's Univ., Belfast).

Fragmentary Collection of Carolan tunes, lacking title-page and other pages,
Dublin   1748   (NLI)

Samuel, Anne and Peter Thompson: *The Hibernian Muse*, London c.1787.

From a Painting in the Possession of Mr. Hardiman, Author of the History of Galway.   J. Martyn, Sculpt. Dublin,

CAROLAN,
The Celebrated Irish Bard.

To His Excellency the Marquess Wellesley, K.G.

LORD-LIEUTENANT of IRELAND &c. &c.

This Print (by Permission) is most respectfully Inscribed, by his most Obedient Servant,

John Martyn

Published as the Act directs Nov.r 1st 1822, by J.Martyn, 24 Lower Ormond Quay Dublin.

John Lee: *A Favourite Collection of the so much admired old Irish Tunes, the original and genuine compositions of Carolan, the celebrated Irish Bard. Set for the harpsichord, violin and German Flute.* Dublin 1780 (NLI).

14

John Lee: *A Favourite Collection of the so much admired old Irish Tunes, the original and genuine compositions of Carolan, the celebrated Irish Bard. Set for the harpsichord, violin and German Flute,* Dublin 1780 (NLI).

'Nancy Cooper' and *'Charles Coote'* — two pages from the Bunting MSS. *(Queen's Univ., Belfast).*

Edward Bunting: *A General Collection of the Ancient Irish Music*, Dublin 1796.

62

Maghstreas ini Breitamain

MAGHISTREAS INI BHREITHAMHAIN. ———— MADAM JUDGE

MAESTOSO

Planzstiz ini Breitamain.

PLANGSTIGH INI BHREITHAMHAIN. ———— PLANXTY JUDGE

ALLEGRO

Edward Bunting: *A General Collection of the Ancient Music of Ireland*, London 1809.

18

John Mulholland: *Collection of Ancient Irish Airs*, Belfast 1810 (Queen's Univ., Belfast).

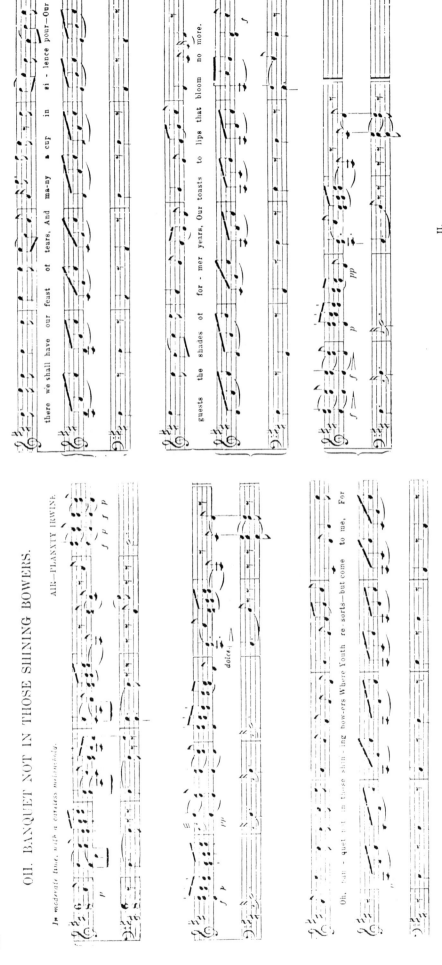

OH. BANQUET NOT IN THOSE SHINING BOWERS.

II.

There, while the myrtle's withering boughs
    Their lifeless leaves around us shed,
We'll brim the bowl to broken vows.
    To friends long lost, the changed, the dead!
Or, as some blighted laurel waves
    Its branches o'er the dreary spot.
We'll drink to those neglected graves,
    Where Valour sleeps, unnamed, forgot:

Moore's *Irish Melodies* — 1879 edition.

20

Carolan's Compositions

uaill cuma eogan Ruaid ua niall.   THE LAMENTATION OF OWEN ROE O'NEILL.

an taoiseac ua catain.   CAPTAIN O'KANE.

caitilin og.   YOUNG CATHERINE.

toirdealac og mic doncad.   YOUNG TERENCE MAC DONOUGH.

O'Neill's *Music of Ireland*, Chicago 1903.

Planxty Toby Peyton

Sergt. Jas. O'Neill

Among the compositions of Carolan the last of the Bards, noted down by Edward Bunting at the Belfast Harp Festival in 1792, was "Planxty Toby Peyton", as played by Hugh Higgins; but it was not published until his third collection, *The Ancient Music of Ireland* appeared in 1840.

Bunting's setting with two others of distinctly different arrangement, was printed in *O'Neills Music of Ireland, Chicago, 1903*. The third setting which is here reproduced was known to John McFadden hailing from County Mayo, and to Sergt. Jas. O'Neill from County Down. Both had learned the tune in practically identical notation in their youth, and both played it in a style to indicate that whoever evolved the flowing rhythmic variant from the Bard's original composition, was a versatile musical genius.

O'Neill's *Waifs and Strays of Gaelic Melody*, Chicago 1922.

DENNIS CONNOR, in Little Chrift-church-yard, Dublin, fells Jewel and Silver Work in the neweft Tafte, Variety of Gilt Buttons, beft Steel Spurs, Canes, Whips, Velvet Caps with Leather Sculls, Roman Fiddle Strings, Harpfichord Wire, with all Kinds of choice Toys, makes German Flutes, Hautboys, and Concert Flutes in the moft exact Manner, and has lately imported Fiddles of all Prices, and other Inftruments, together with printed Mufick fitted for all Capacities, having a Correfpondent in London will continue to fell the Monthly Mafques as they come out. —— N.B. Said Connor has agreed with Mr. Carolan, Son to the celebrated Mr. Terence Carolan, in publifhing the Compofitions of his faid Father, and there is now finifhed a Book containing 61 Pieces of Mufick which is to be fold only by faid Connor and Carolan, and Subfcriptions for other Books of faid Compofition to be taken in by faid Connor and Carolan, and by Michael Handbury, Engraver, at the Bear in George's-lane.

Advertisement in Faulkners Dublin Journal, June 14-18, 1748

Tunes for Patrons

1. Lady Athenry

Grazioso

2. Mrs. Bermingham *First Air*

Andantino

3. Mrs. Bermingham *Second Air*

4. James Betagh

Jig. *Vivace*

5. Lady Blayney

Allegro

6. George Brabazon *First Air*

Joviale

7. George Brabazon *Second Air*

Moderato

8. Sir Ulick Burke

Allegro moderato

9. Sir Festus Burke

10. Lady Laetitia Burke

11. The Honourable Thomas Burke

12. Isabella Burke

32

13. Thomas Burke

14. Planxty Burke

15. Mrs. Cole

16. Nancy Cooper *First Air*

17. Nancy Cooper *Second Air*

18. Sir Charles Coote

19. Edward Corcoran

20. Mrs. Costello

21. Planxty Crilly

Allegro commodo

22. Sir Edward Crofton

Moderato

23. James Crofton

Allegro ma non troppo

24. Mrs. Crofton

25. Miss Crofton

26. Bridget Cruise *First Air*

Andante

27. Bridget Cruise *Second Air*

Andante maestoso

28. Bridget Cruise *Third Air*

Andante con moto

29. Bridget Cruise *Fourth Air*

30. Richard Cusack

31. James Daly

32. Dr. Delany

Grave

Allegro moderato

33. Mrs. Delany

Allegro moderato

34. Lord Dillon

Moderato

35. Lady Dillon

Allegro moderato

Jig. Allegro

44

36. Gerald Dillon

37. Fanny Dillon

38. Counsellor Dillon

39. Luke Dillon

40. Edward Dodwell

Allegro moderato

41. Planxty Drew

Allegretto

42. John Drury *First Air*

Vivace

43. John Drury *Second Air*

44. William Eccles

45. Mrs. Edwards

46. Mrs. Fallon

47. Mrs. Farrell

48. Miss Fetherston, or Carolan's Devotion

49. Mrs. Garvey *First Air*

50. Mrs. Garvey *Second Air*

Andante moderato

51. Lady Gethin

Allegretto

52. Miss Goulding

53. Dr. John Hart, Bishop of Achonry

54. Mrs. Harwood

55. Robert Hawkes

56. Hewlett

57. Captain Higgins

Jig. *Più mosso*

58. Lord Inchiquin

Moderato ma con anima

59. Colonel John Irwin

Allegretto

60. Colonel Irwin

61. John Jameson

62. Baptist Johnston

63. John Jones

64. Loftus Jones

65. Thomas Morres Jones, or Bumper Squire Jones

66. Robert Jordan

67. Thomas Judge, or Carolan's Frolic

68. Mrs. Judge

69. Mrs. Keel

70. Daniel Kelly

71. Hugh Kelly

72. John Kelly

Allegretto grazioso

73. Mabel Kelly

Poco andante

74. Patrick Kelly

75. Susanna Kelly

76. Planxty Kelly

77. Lord Louth

78. Henry MacDermott Roe *First Air*

79. Henry MacDermott Roe *Second Air*

80. Henry MacDermott Roe *Third Air*

Allegro

81. Mrs. MacDermott Roe

Allegretto

82. Mrs. Anne MacDermott Roe

83. Elizabeth MacDermott Roe

84. Father Brian MacDermott Roe

85. Edmond MacDermott Roe

Allegro moderato

86. John MacDermott

Allegretto

87. Miss MacDermott, or The Princess Royal

Allegretto

88. Dolly MacDonough

Andante con moto

89. Dr. MacMahon, Bishop of Clogher

Risoluto

90. Miss MacMurray

Allegretto grazioso

91. Betty MacNeill

Allegretto

92. Morgan Magan

Vivace

93. Captain Magan

Allegretto

94. Kitty Magennis

Moderato

95. Brian Maguire

96. Constantine Maguire

97. Mr. Malone

98. Margaret Malone

Andantino

99. Catherine Martin

100. Lord Massereene

101. Mrs. Maxwell *First Air*

102. Mrs. Maxwell *Second Air*

103. John Moore

Vivace

Jig. Poco più mosso

104. Peggy Morton

Allegretto

105. Miss Murphy

Allegretto

106. Miss Noble

Allegretto

107. John Nugent

108. Mrs. Nugent

109. Elizabeth Nugent

Allegretto

110. Grace Nugent

Allegretto

Jig. *Vivace ma non troppo*

114. John O' Connor

115. Maurice O' Connor *First Air*

116. Maurice O' Connor *Second Air*

117. Maurice O' Connor *Third Air*

118. Mrs. O' Connor

119. Dr. O' Connor

120. Michael O' Connor *First Air*

Con brio

Jig. *Allegretto*

88

121. Michael O' Connor *Second Air*

122. Denis O' Conor *First Air*

123. Denis O' Conor *Second Air*

Allegro assai

124. Mrs. O' Conor

125. Charles O' Conor

126. Colonel Manus O' Donnell

127. Hugh O' Donnell

128. O' Flinn

129. Colonel O' Hara

130. Kean O' Hara *First Air*

131. Kean O' Hara *Second Air*

132. Kean O' Hara *Third Air*

133. Captain O' Kain

134. Katherine O' More

135. Mrs. O' Neill of Carlane

136. Mrs. O' Neill

137. Mary O' Neill, or Carolan's Favourite Jig

138. O' Reilly of Athcarne

139. Conor O' Reilly

140. John O' Reilly *First Air*

141. John O' Reilly *Second Air*

142. Owen O' Rourke

143. Mrs. O' Rourke

144. Planxty O' Rourke *First Air*

145. Planxty O' Rourke *Second Air*

Moderato

146. Frank Palmer

Allegretto

147. Squire Parsons

Allegro moderato

148. Tobias Peyton

Allegretto

149. John Peyton

150. Eleanor Plunkett

151. James Plunkett

152. Planxty Plunkett

153. David Power

154. Mrs. Power, or Carolan's Concerto

155. Fanny Power

Grazioso

156. Mervyn Pratt

Allegretto

157. George Reynolds

Allegretto

158. Lady St. John

Moderato

108

159. Sir Arthur Shaen

160. Major Shanly

161. Dr. John Stafford, or Carolan's Receipt

Con spirito

162. Mrs. Sterling

Allegro ma non troppo

163. Captain Sudley, or Carolan's Dowry

Allegro

164. Planxty Sweeny

Allegretto

165. Mr. Waller

Allegretto

volti

166. Mrs. Waller

Allegro vivace

167. William Ward

Allegretto

168. Planxty Wilkinson

Moderato

169. Lady Wrixon

Allegretto

170. General Wynne

Tunes without Titles

171.

172.

volti

173.

174.

175.

176.

177.

Moderato

178.

Animato

179.

180.

Miscellaneous Tunes

181. All Alive

182. Blind Mary

183. Carolan's Cap

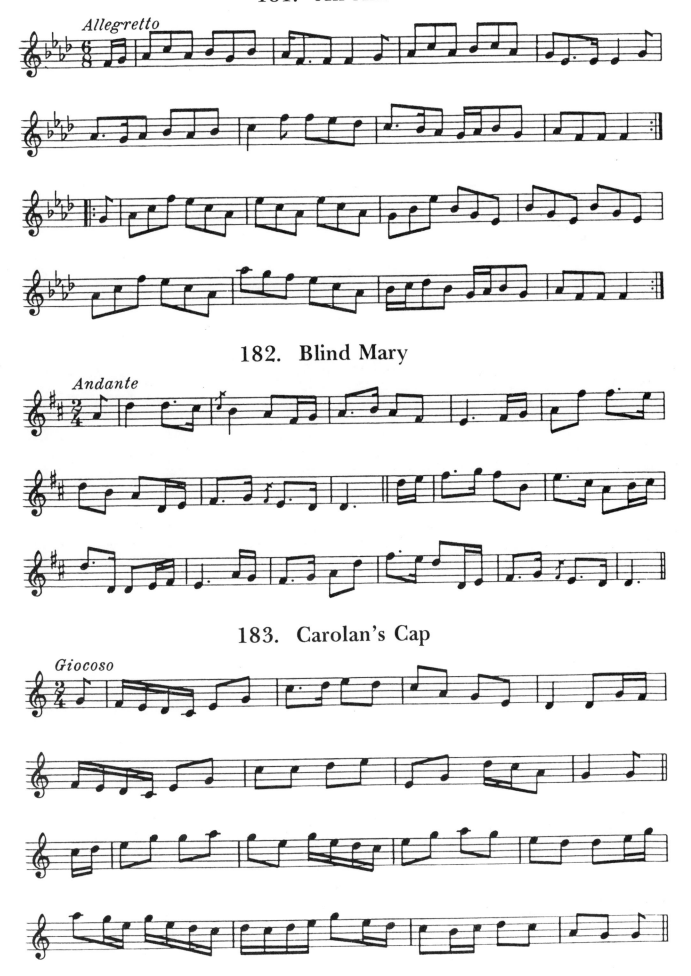

184. Carolan's Cottage

Andante

185. Carolan's Cup

Moderato

186. Carolan's Draught

Allegro con spirito

187. Carolan's Dream

Moderato

188. Carolan's Farewell to Music

189. Carolan's Maggot

190. Carolan's Quarrel with the Landlady

Con fuoco

191. Carolan's Ramble to Cashel

Andante

192. Cremonea

Andante

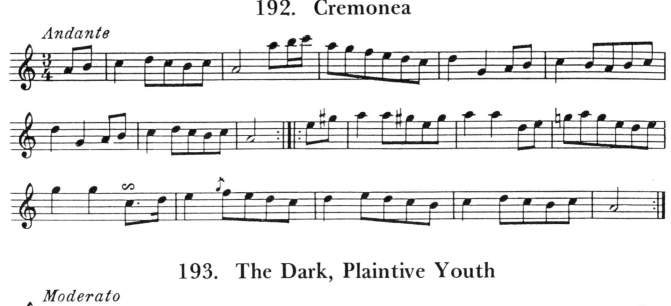

193. The Dark, Plaintive Youth

Moderato

194. The Elevation

Largo

Poco più mosso

195. The Fairy Queen

Andante con moto

volti

196. The Landlady

197. Ode to Whiskey

198. One Bottle More

Vivace

199. The O' Rourkes' Feast

Vivace

200. The Seas are Deep

201. Separation of Soul and Body

202. Sheebeg and Sheemore

203. The Two William Davises

204. Variations on the Scottish Air " Cock up your Beaver "

The air from the *Scots Musical Museum*

Allegretto

Variations attributed to Carolan

volti

205. Variations on the Scottish Air " When she cam ben "

The air from the *Scots Musical Museum*

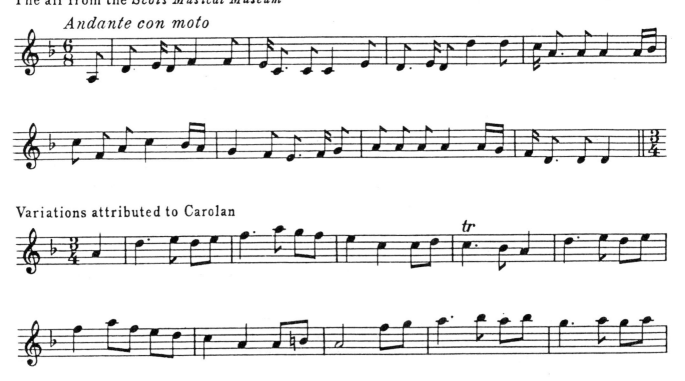

Laments

206. Lament for Sir Ulick Burke

207. The Clergy's Lamentation

208. Lord Galway's Lamentation

144

209. Lament for Charles MacCabe

Andante

210. Lament for Terence MacDonough

Andante maestoso

211. Lament for Owen Roe O' Neill

Andante maestoso

212. Lament for Owen O' Rourke

213. Squire Wood's Lamentation on the Refusal of his Halfpence

A recent Discovery

214. Captain O' Neill

The above is a recently discovered Carolan composition from a manuscript compiled by the MacLean-Clephane sisters of Torloik, on the island of Mull (c.1816) — See 'Ceol, a Journal of Irish Music' Vol. VI, April 1983.

From John Derrick's 'Image of Ireland' 1581.

Sources of the Tunes

Printed Music Collections

John and William Neal *A Collection of the Most Celebrated Irish Tunes proper for the Violin, German Flute or Hautboy*. Dublin c.1724.

Dan. Wright. *Aria Di Camera. Being a Choice Collection of Scotch, Irish and Welsh Airs for the Violin and German Flute by the following Masters: Mr Alex, Urquahart, of Edinburgh; Mr Dermt. O'Connor, of Limerick; Mr Hugh Edwards, of Carmarthen*. London. c.1730.

Burk Thumoth. *Twelve English and Twelve Irish Airs*. London. 1745-50.

John Lee. *A Favourite Collection of the so much admired old Irish Tunes, the original and genuine compositions of Carolan, the celebrated Irish Bard. Set for the harpsichord, violin and German-flute*. Dublin 1780.

Joseph Cooper Walker. *Historical Memoirs of the Irish Bards*. Dublin 1786, Second edition (in two volumes) Dublin 1818.

Samuel, Anne and Peter Thompson. *The Hibernian Muse; a Collection of Irish Airs, including the Most Favourite Compositions of Carolan, The Celebrated Irish Bard*. London c.1786.

Edward Bunting. *A General Collection of the Ancient Irish Music*. London 1796.

O'Farrell. *Collection of National Irish Music for the Union Pipes*. London c.1797-1800.

Smollet Holden. *A Collection of Old-Established Irish Slow and Quick Tunes*. Books I & II. Dublin 1806-7.

Edward Bunting. *A General Collection of the Ancient Music of Ireland*. London 1809.

John Mulholland. *Collection of Ancient Irish Airs*. Belfast 1810.

Edward Bunting. *The Ancient Music of Ireland*. Dublin 1840.

The Citizen, or Dublin Monthly Magazine. 1841-3.

George Petrie. *Ancient Music of Ireland*. Dublin 1855.

Charles Stanford. *Complete Petrie Collection of Ancient Irish Music*. London, Parts I & II, 1902, Part III, 1905.

Francis O'Neill. *Music of Ireland.* Chicago 1903.

P.W. Joyce. *Old Irish Folk Music & Songs.* London 1909.

D.J. O'Sullivan. *The Bunting Collection of Irish Folk Music and Songs.* Edited from the Original Manuscripts. (for the Irish Folk Song Society). London Parts I-VI 1927-39.

Manuscript sources:

The Bunting MSS. in the Library of Queen's University, Belfast.

The Forde MSS. in the Royal Irish Academy, Dublin.

The Pigot MSS. in the Royal Irish Academy, Dublin.

The Petrie MSS. in the National Museum, Dublin.

The Hudson MSS. in the Public Library of Boston, Massachusetts.

The Goodman MSS. in the Library of Trinity College, Dublin.

The Joyce MSS. in the National Library, Dublin.

Bibliography

Edward Bunting — *Ancient Irish Music,* Dublin 1796
Ancient Music of Ireland, Dublin 1809
Ancient Music of Ireland, Dublin 1840
(re-issued by Waltons of Dublin in one volume, 1969)

D.J. O'Sullivan — *The Bunting Collection of Irish Folk Music and Songs,*
Journal of the Irish Folk Song Society, Vols XXII-XXVII
London ,1927-1939

D.J. O'Sullivan — *Carolan. The Life, Times and Music of an Irish Harper,*
two volumes, Routledge and Kegan Paul, London 1958.
(reprinted by Celtic Music, Louth, England 1983)

R.B. Armstrong — *The Irish and Highland Harps,* Edinburgh 1904
(re-issued by Irish University Press, Dublin 1969)

Joan Rimmer — *The Irish Harp,* Mercier Press, Cork 1969

Richard Hayward — *The Story of the Irish Harp,* London 1954

Tomás Ó Máille — *Amhráin Chearbhalláin,* Irish Texts Society, Vol.XVII,
London 1915.

Charlotte M. Fox — *Annals of the Irish Harpers,* London 1911.

Breandán Ó Buachalla — *I mBéal Feirste Cois Cuain,* Clóchomhar,
Báile Átha Cliath 1968

Gráinne Yeats — *The Belfast Harpers Festival 1792,* Gael Linn, Dublin 1980

Nicholas Carolan — *A Collection of the most Celebrated Irish Tunes
proper for the violin, German flute or hautboy.*
Dublin 1724. (facsimile edition)
Folk Music Society of Ireland, Dublin 1986

Performing Editions of Carolan's Music

*Music by Carolan, arranged for recorder and keyboard, with optional part
for cello, viola da gamba, bassoon or bass recorder,* by Douglas Gunn,
Ossian Publications, Cork 1983. Also suitable for flute, violin, oboe.

O'Carolan, Three Suites arranged for Solo Guitar, by Andrew Sheils,
Ossian Publications, Cork 1984

Irish Music by O'Carolan, arranged for Recorder Trio, by Douglas Gunn,
Ossian Publications, Cork 1986

Discography

Although many records will include one or two of Carolan's pieces, the following LP's are entirely devoted to his music and are still available.

Carolan agus Ceolta eile, The Douglas Gunn Ensemble, Gael Linn CEF 077
Carolan's Receipt Derek Bell, Claddagh CC18
Carolan's Favourite, Derek Bell, Claddagh CC28
The Music of O'Carolan, Various artists, Shanachie 95009

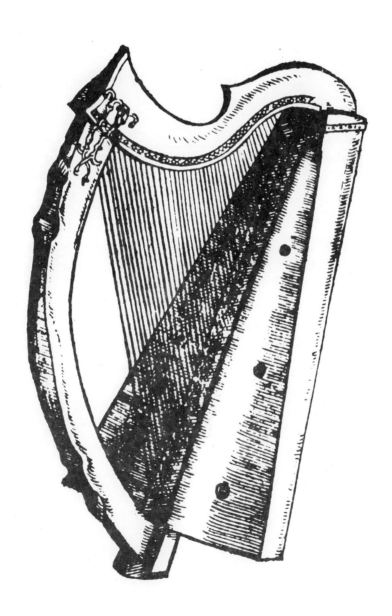

Index of the Tunes

Titles in each Section in Alphabetical Order

Tunes for Patrons

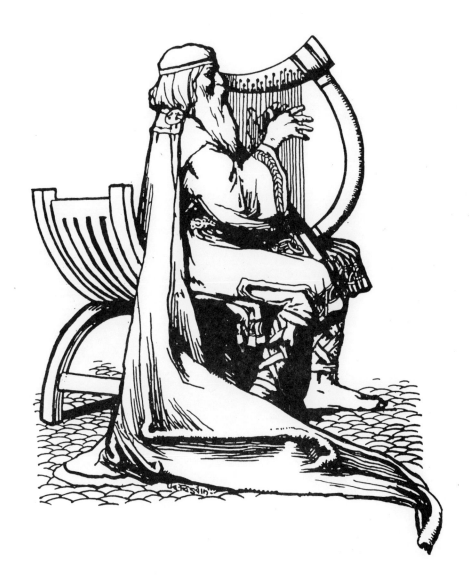

For our complete catalogue of Irish & General Music Books, Sheets and Audio Tapes published and Distributed by us send your address and an (international) postal reply coupon to:

Ossian Publications, P.O. Box 84, Cork, Ireland

*Books published include works for Violin, Flute, Guitar, Piano, Irish Songbooks,
Tutors for various instruments, Collections of Traditional Music, Choral works.*